Forestry Commission
Handbook 2

Trees and Weeds

Weed control for successful tree establishment

By R.J. Davies

Silviculturist, Forestry Commission

LONDON: HER MAJESTY'S STATIONERY OFFICE

HMSO BOOKS

HMSO publications are available from:

HMSO Publications Centre
(Mail and telephone orders only)
PO Box 276, London, SW8 5DT
Telephone orders 01-622 3316
General enquiries 01-211 5656
(queuing system in operation for both numbers)

HMSO Bookshops
49 High Holborn, London, WC1V 6HB   01-211 5656 (Counter service only)
258 Broad Street, Birmingham, B1 2HE   021-643 3740
Southey House, 33 Wine Street, Bristol, BS1 2BQ   (0272) 264306
9-21 Princess Street, Manchester, M60 8AS   061-834 7201
80 Chichester Street, Belfast, BT1 4JY   (0232) 238451
71-73 Lothian Road, Edinburgh, EH3 9AZ   031-228 4181

HMSO's Accredited Agents
(see Yellow Pages)

and through good booksellers

ISBN 0 11 710208 3

ODC 441 : 414.12 : 236.1 : 27

Keywords
Weeds, Establishment, Weed control, Arboriculture, Forestry

Published in 1987
European Year of the Environment

Acknowledgements

The following research foresters have borne the brunt of implementing my weeding experiments: M W Allen, K F Baker, P R Barwick, I H Blackmore, S M Colderick, T D Cooper, K A S Gabriel, J B H Gardiner, R E J Howes, D J Lyons, J D McNeill, S E Malone, D G Rogers, A L Sharpe, J P Stannard and R E Warn. Without their help it would have been impossible to establish the well-replicated experiments described in this Handbook. Many of the views expressed have arisen through discussions with them and other colleagues. Miss E H Crompton and M W Silver helped me to investigate the effects of weeds on moisture stress in trees. R C Boswell gave statistical advice on the design and interpretation of the experiments. Many of the photographs were taken by G L Gate and S E Malone. The Department of Transport, the Property Services Agency, Milton Keynes Development Corporation, the Greater London Council, West Yorkshire Metropolitan County Council, Bedford County Council and the London Brick Company provided sites for some of the experiments. Much of the research was funded by the Department of the Environment.

Enquiries relating to this publication should be addressed to the Technical Publications Officer, Forestry Commission Research Station, Alice Holt Lodge, Wrecclesham, Farnham, Surrey GU10 4LH

Contents

PLATE 1
Newly planted rowans growing well, aided by effective chemical weed control. (They are in a staking experiment; hence the giant stakes in the background.)

PLATE 2
An expensive eyesore. Mown grass close to the base of these trees is probably largely responsible for the deaths, die-back and sparse foliage.

Introduction

A weed is a plant growing where it is not wanted. Weeds can be small or large: moss growing in a lawn, thistles in a flower bed and birch in a pine plantation may all be weeds. On landscaped sites, where appearance is paramount, plants may become weeds merely by looking untidy; Giant hogweed might fall in this category. Other plants such as Creeping thistle and ragwort are defined as 'injurious weeds' in the 1959 Weeds Act because they pose a threat to agricultural production, and occupiers of land may be required to prevent their spread. This Handbook concentrates on those weeds which are weeds because they reduce the survival and growth of young trees.

Grassy swards are established on many landscaped sites to reduce soil erosion and provide an attractive green appearance. To achieve these objectives they contain vigorous agricultural varieties of grass and legume species. Such swards seriously interfere with the growth of young trees, but since they were established intentionally it is perhaps debatable whether the plants in them are 'weeds'. A compromise between the conflicting objectives of growing trees and turf is needed.

Although landscape trees are not grown as a commercial crop where maximum growth rates are sought, rapid growth is still desirable. Large trees have higher landscape values than small trees; rapid growth hastens the attainment of these values. Large trees may be planted to produce an instant effect, but if as a result of weed interference they die or only just survive they create an eyesore (Plate 2). Effective weeding promotes rapid growth and tree health, and healthy trees look attractive. Faster growth also means the tree is vulnerable to vandals and other damaging agents for a shorter time.

This Handbook presents the conclusions and recommendations arising from over 30 arboricultural weeding experiments conducted since 1977. The results of a few of these experiments are given in Tables and Figures*. These show, more clearly than words could, just how severely weeds harm young trees.

How do weeds reduce tree survival and growth? 'Interference' is often a better word to describe their effects than 'competition', since it implies no presuppositions about the mechanisms involved. Weeds do compete for moisture, nutrients and light; but they may also interfere with trees by releasing toxins, modifying soil and air temperatures and harbouring pests. Because many of these factors, and doubtless others of which we are oblivious, operate simultaneously, it is tempting to merely describe the symptoms – tree survival, health and growth – and ignore the causes. Nevertheless, some knowledge of *how* weeds interfere with trees is needed if appropriate weeding methods are to be selected. This Handbook is therefore divided into two parts: the first discusses some of the ways in which weeds interfere with young trees; the second describes methods of controlling weeds.

---

* For the sake of clarity only the average survival and growth data are shown in the Tables and Figures, details of the experimental design and statistical analysis being omitted. Where an experiment is cited in support of a statement made in the text, then the relevant treatment means differed significantly; at least at $p < 0.05$ and usually at the $p < 0.001$ probability level.

How weeds influence young trees

On most landscaped sites in Britain competition for moisture and nutrients appears to be the most important factor. Since nutrient availability is often limited by soil dryness, competition for soil moisture is discussed first and in greater detail than other mechanisms of weed interference.

Competition for soil moisture

In dry summer weather grass close to the ground often feels damp, while bare soil surfaces feel deceptively dry and may crack. But the soil beneath grass or other vegetation is invariably drier than the soil from a comparable area with no vegetation. Thus, trees growing among weeds find it harder to extract soil moisture than those in bare soil.

Weeds dry the soil by extracting moisture through their roots and transpiring it from their leaves into the atmosphere. Weeds also intercept rainfall, some of which evaporates before it reaches the soil. In the absence of vegetation, moisture evaporates rapidly from a damp soil surface, but once a skin of dry soil forms, further evaporation is very slow.

Weeds continue to dry the soil even if they are cut back regularly. On grassy sites, mowing helps to maintain the sward's vigour, and often results in even drier soil than under unmown grass. Mown grass is therefore very injurious to young trees. (Figure 1 refers to an experiment in which regularly mown grass dried the soil more than unmown grass.) By contrast, cutting vegetation in which grasses are not dominant usually reduces competition for soil moisture with newly planted trees; but because the weeds are not killed such competition is only reduced, not removed.

Although most soil moisture is lost by transpiration, some evaporates from bare soil surfaces. Mulching reduces this and, in the absence of weeds or trees growing in or through the mulch, may keep the soil near field capacity all through the summer (Figure 1). (A soil is at 'field capacity' when it is holding as much water as it can against the pull of gravity.)

Moisture stress in trees

Since weeds compete with trees for moisture one might expect unweeded trees to suffer greater internal moisture stress than weeded trees. Moisture stress (the sub-atmospheric pressure, or the tension, of the water in the plant) can be measured using a pressure chamber (Figure 2). Although such assessments some-times show unweeded trees to be under greater stress than weeded trees, frequently there is little difference. Trees avoid moisture stress in various ways. Firstly, the stomata of unweeded trees stay closed longer than those of trees enjoying greater soil moisture availability. Even the stomata of healthy trees with plentiful soil moisture close in the middle of a hot summer's day, but they re-open readily when the sun's strength declines in the afternoon. Figure 3 shows the effect of grass, and irrigation, on trees' stomata (but because there was no convenient sunny day in 1986 it was not possible to illustrate midday stomatal closure in Figure 3).

Unweeded trees also avoid moisture stress by developing less foliage than well-weeded trees, hence reducing their water needs; they form smaller leaves, complete their shoot growth earlier in the season (thus producing fewer leaves) and some-times shed leaves prematurely. Often, whole branches of unweeded trees die; such trees have much less foliage to support. The effects of weeds on the amount of foliage carried by trees are illustrated in Table 1, Plates 15 and 16 and on the Front Cover.

Moisture stress is not avoided cheaply. A tree with little foliage and stomata that are shut for long periods can barely photo-synthesise; and since photosynthates are needed for root growth, and root growth is required for water uptake, a vicious circle may develop resulting in die-back and eventual death of the unweeded tree. The situation is even worse because reduced leaf and bud activity in turn reduces the production of the hormones that control root growth. Healthy shoot growth is generally associated with healthy root growth, but it is usually difficult to determine whether the roots are responding to the shoots, or the shoots to the roots.

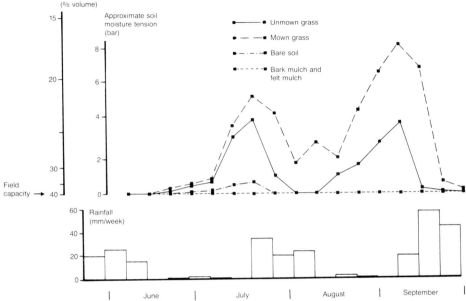

Approximate soil
moisture content
(% volume)

Approximate soil
moisture tension
(bar)

■—■ Unmown grass
■- - ■ Mown grass
■-·-■ Bare soil
■······■ Bark mulch and
felt mulch

Field
capacity →

Rainfall
(mm/week)

| June | July | August | September |

FIGURE 1
Soil moisture content and tension at 100
mm depth under various weeding regimes
through summer 1981.

Taken from Davies (1985). Soil moisture
status was assessed indirectly by the
electrical resistance of gypsum blocks. The
site was a silty clay loam at Alice Holt,
Hampshire. Bare soil and mulched plots
were kept weed-free with paraquat.

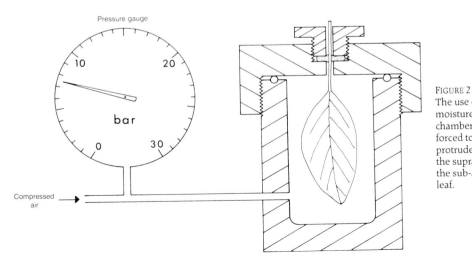

Pressure gauge

bar

Compressed
air

FIGURE 2
The use of a pressure chamber to measure
moisture stress in trees. Air pressure in the
chamber is slowly increased until sap is
forced to the cut end of the petiole which
protrudes from the chamber. At this point
the supra-atmospheric air pressure balances
the sub-atmospheric water tension in the
leaf.

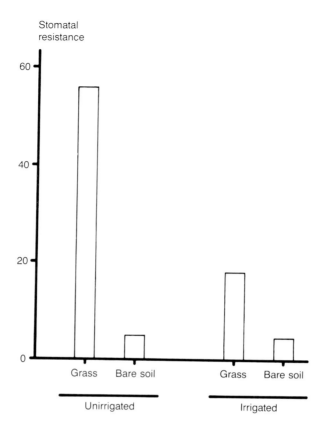

Stomatal resistance

FIGURE 3

The effects of grass sward and irrigation on stomatal resistance (the resistance of the lower leaf surface to loss of water by transpiration) of Norway maple on 23 July 1986. The stomata of most trees in unirrigated grass were closed, irrigation helped considerably, but trees in bare soil had their stomata open, and could therefore photosynthesise freely, even without irrigation.

The maple transplants were planted in April 1986 in a clay loam at Alice Holt, Hampshire. Irrigated grass and bare soil plots received 103 and 66 mm of water respectively between May and 17 July 1986, these being the depths required to maintain small soil moisture deficits of about 30 mm. Stomatal resistance (s/cm) was assessed using a diffusion porometer at various times of day on 23 July, the results being averaged here. Bare soil plots were kept bare with paraquat. The grass was cut occasionally to keep it below the trees' foliage.

Effects of weeds on root and shoot growth

It is often said that plants develop more root and less shoot in response to drought; if weeds compete with trees for moisture then they might be expected to exert a similar effect. However, excavation of trees from a weeding experiment showed that weeds reduced root growth as much as shoot growth (Figures 4 and 5, and Plates 3 and 4). Differences in root : shoot ratio were unclear, and they are hard to interpret because even under uniform conditions the ratio falls as the tree grows from seed to maturity. What is clear is that weed interference reduces both root and shoot growth.

Climate modifies effects of competition for moisture

The climate modifies the harm weeds do to trees: competition for soil moisture is less important where the climate results in smaller soil moisture deficits. ('Soil moisture deficit' is the depth of water needed to re-wet the soil to field capacity.) Nevertheless, weeds have reduced tree growth in arboricultural weeding experiments to a similar extent in dry areas (eg. near Cambridge – see Plates 3 and 4) and areas with high annual rainfall (such as Dartmoor and central Lancashire). This may be because even high rainfall sites frequently experience large soil moisture deficits in summer. Since few landscaping schemes are in areas with very high rainfall, virtually all landscape trees are susceptible to weed-induced moisture shortages.

Irrigation and competition for moisture

Irrigation reduces weed-induced soil moisture shortages, and lessens the harm done by weeds (Figure 3). However, it is expensive and water is least available during prolonged droughts when it is most needed. Too much irrigation leaches nutrients from freely drained sandy sites, and kills tree roots through water-logging on poorly drained sites. At best, irrigation is a supplement, not an alternative, to effective weeding. Indeed it often stimulates weed seed germination. It is most useful on sites with very poor moisture retention or in exceptionally severe droughts (if water is available) or for the most prestigious planting schemes, rather than as a specification for all schemes.

If trees are to be irrigated, it is important to do so *before* drought damage occurs. Trees planted late in the planting season are particularly sensitive to spring drought; irrigation in April,

Table 1 The influence of six weeding regimes on first-year growth, and second-year leaf area and foliar nitrogen concentrations, of Silver maple transplants

		1984 growth		Foliage assessment in July 1985			
		Height (cm)	Diameter (mm)	Leaves/tree (number)	Size (mm²/leaf)	Area/tree (m²/tree)	N concentration (% dry weight)
1	Unmown sward	1.2	−0.1	57	2570	0.13	1.8
2	Mown sward	−0.8	0.4	55	3052	0.17	1.7
3	Unmown clover	−0.1	0.4	81	3568	0.27	2.3
4	1 m diam. herbicide	38.8	5.0	290	7093	1.85	2.6
5	1 m diam. polythene	40.9	5.8	289	6305	1.55	2.4
6	Total herbicide	58.1	7.8	360	7547	2.65	3.5

This experiment was planted in February 1984 on a loam at Alice Holt, Hampshire. The mown and unmown swards were predominantly grasses. The clover in treatment 3 was *Trifolium repens* 'Huia'. Paraquat and glyphosate were used to keep 1 m diameter spots and whole plots weed-free in treatments 4 and 6. Black polythene mulches in treatment 5 had their corners buried, giving octagons of about 1 m diameter. The sward surrounding the herbicide spots and polythene mats was mown. Trees in clover grew better in 1985 than 1984, probably because the clover did not resume growth after winter until May 1985, thus giving the trees an interference-free start to the second season. (Leaf area per tree is the mean leaf area of 24 trees in each treatment, not the product of mean leaf number and mean leaf size: hence the apparent discrepancy.) (There is a photograph of this experiment on the front cover.)

May or June may help them re-establish their root system, and so withstand the greater soil moisture deficits that occur in midsummer.

Soil type modifies effects of competition for moisture

Soils vary in their ability to retain and release moisture to plants; thus soil type also modifies the harm weeds do to trees. As water is lost by transpiration and evaporation, soil moisture content falls and moisture tension rises. As the soil moisture tension rises plants experience increasing difficulty in extracting moisture, until at the permanent wilting point (about 15 bar* for most plants) any remaining water is unavailable to plants. The quantity of water stored by a soil between field capacity (about 0.05 bar in

most British soils) and the permanent wilting point is the soil's 'available water capacity'. The relationship between soil moisture content and tension, and thus the soil's available water capacity, is largely determined by soil texture (Figure 6) although it also varies with soil structure, compaction and organic matter content. (Texture is defined by the sizes of the mineral particles in the soil.)

Of the three soils in Figure 6 the clay holds most moisture, but because much of this is held at tensions over 15 bar its available water capacity is little higher than that of the sand. Moreover, since much of the clay's available water is held at tensions above 2 bar, plants, especially newly planted plants, have difficulty using it. (The sand in Figure 6 has an available water capacity of 11 per cent, 110 mm of water in each metre of soil, or if one assumes young trees are tapping the upper 300 mm of soil this is equivalent to 33 mm of rain.) Because sands retain water and nutrients so poorly, weed growth is sparse and weak. Nevertheless, sparse weed growth on a sand frequently reduces tree growth more than lush vigorous weeds on, for example, a silt loam. (Plate 15 shows

---

* Bar = a unit of pressure, or tension, approximately equal to average atmospheric pressure at sea level.

PLATES 3 & 4
Oak trees excavated three seasons after planting as 38 cm transplants in a weeding experiment near Cambridge. Tree on the left had no weeding. Tree on the right grew in a 0.5 m diameter weed-free spot.
(See also Figure 4 which refers to the same experiment.)

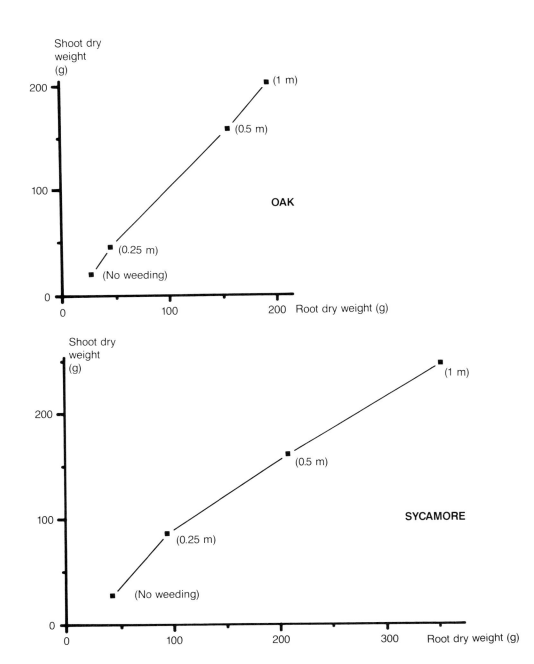

The effect of weeding different diameter areas around the base of oak and sycamore transplants on the trees' root and shoot development.

Trees were excavated in late 1984 after three growing seasons from a grassy site on a fine-textured soil beside the M11 motorway near Cambridge. Spots of 0.25, 0.5 and 1 m diameter were kept fairly weed-free using paraquat and glyphosate. (Accidental herbicide damage to the oak in the 0.25 m treatment partially balanced the relief from weed interference.) (See also Plates 3 and 4.)

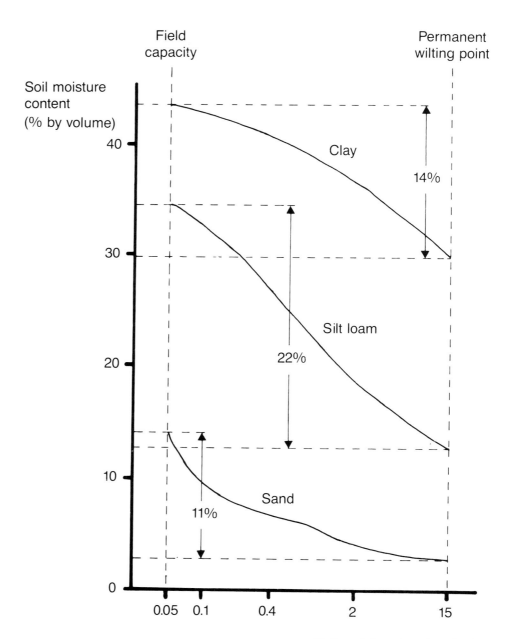

Table 2 The effect of three weeding regimes on survival, height and diameter of Italian alder transplants and unrooted Violet willow cuttings after 2 years on a soil with very poor moisture retention

	Alder			Willow		
	Survival (%)	Height (cm)	Diameter (mm)	Survival (%)	Height (cm)	Diameter (mm)
0.5 m diameter herbicide spots	6	39	6	4	19	2
2 m wide herbicide strips	27	46	7	39	68	7
1.2 m wide black polythene in 2 m herbicide strips	67	84	15	99	152	19

This experiment was planted in March 1981 beside the M275 motorway near Portsmouth, on an embankment built of sand and covered with a thin layer of top-soil. Herbicide spots and strips were kept fairly weed-free with propyzamide and paraquat. Herbicide along the edges of the polythene mulch strips prevented weeds rooting under the mulch. (Most of the deaths of the mulched alder were caused by voles which nested under the polythene.)

the effects of sparse weed growth on sycamore growing in sand.) Survival may be greatly reduced by weeds on soils with poor moisture storage. Table 2 illustrates this point; it gives the results of an experiment on a dry sandy embankment where survival of trees around which all weeds within one metre had been killed was better than that of trees with small (0.25 m radius) weed-free areas. (There were no unweeded trees in this experiment because earlier trials had proved that none could survive on the site without being weeded.)

Improving soil moisture retention

Peat or compost is frequently mixed with soil in the planting pit to increase soil moisture storage and help the young tree through dry spells. This sometimes helps, but does not obviate the need to weed; and effective weeding is more important. On sites with very poor drainage, addition of organic matter damages trees; micro-organisms feeding on organic material compete with tree roots for oxygen, which is in short supply in most waterlogged soils.

Polymers which absorb and release large volumes of water have also been advocated to improve soil moisture storage. A few grams of polymer are mixed into each planting pit. Some of these materials will hold hundreds of times their own weight in water, rather like wallpaper paste. However, Forestry Commission experiments testing a range of polymers and other soil ameliorants are showing no benefits from their use. They are certainly no substitute for effective weeding.

Soil conditions on disturbed sites

Many trees are planted on severely disturbed sites, such as land reclaimed after mining, or adjacent to new roads, houses and factories. Earth movement and the passage of machinery compact the soil reducing its moisture storage capacity. These sites are therefore very dry in summer, and any young trees are highly susceptible to weed-induced drought. But because the soil structure has been damaged these same sites are often waterlogged for long periods in winter; the resultant anaerobic soil conditions may kill the deeper tree roots, making the trees very susceptible to weed interference when the soil dries out again. Many experiments have shown that chemical weed control improves tree growth, and often survival also, on such sites. But on poorly drained sites mulching, particularly with organic

Table 3 The effect of organic mulches on the survival of sycamore, Small-leaved lime and Italian alder transplants on badly drained sites

	Survival (%)			
	Sycamore (3)	Lime (3)	Alder (3)	Sycamore (1)
Control	89	85	100	59
Fibre-board 'Tree collar' (45 cm diam., 2 mm thick)	85	65	96	43
Pulverised bark (70 cm diam., 10 cm max. depth)	74	37	87	30
Sewage sludge (70 cm diam., 10 cm max. depth)	69	43	80	11

These experiments were planted in March 1977 on poorly drained sites with damaged soil structure and clayey texture at Milton Keynes. Survival was assessed after three or one growing seasons (indicated in brackets after the species). The sycamore assessed after one season were on an even more poorly drained site than those assessed after three seasons. Mulching exacerbated the anaerobic soil conditions which killed trees.

material, makes the anaerobic soil conditions worse and may kill trees (Table 3). Pre-planting site preparation to provide at least 500 mm of uncompacted, freely draining soil greatly improves tree establishment, and long-term stability, but does not obviate the need to weed.

Competition for nutrients

Young trees growing with weeds often look nutrient deficient. Their leaves are fewer, smaller and yellower than those of well-weeded trees; chemical analysis confirms that the foliage of unweeded trees has lower nutrient concentrations, particularly of nitrogen. (Tables 1 and 4 give the concentrations of some nutrients in the foliage of trees growing in different weeding regimes.) The total nutrient content of well-weeded trees is usually very much greater than that of unweeded trees.

Trees and weeds compete for nutrients, but because moisture and nutrient competition are interrelated the true situation is more complex. Once weeds and trees have dried the soil, plants can no longer extract nutrients from it. The upper soil layers dry out first and since this is where most of the plant-available nutrients are found, weed and tree growth may be checked despite adequate moisture availability at slightly greater depth.

Weeding increases nutrient availability in other ways too. For example, dead weeds release nutrients as they rot. Also, weeding, by its influence on soil moisture and temperature, often accelerates the decomposition process.

Fertiliser application

Since trees and weeds compete for nutrients, one might expect fertilising to be beneficial. However, herbaceous plants are generally more responsive to fertiliser than are woody plants, especially newly planted trees. Young trees in a small patch of vigorous grass which has been stimulated by fertiliser or compost in the planting pit are an all too common sight. Fertilising without weeding can depress tree growth (see Table 5, oak). Hence, young trees should not be fertilised without first killing the weeds.

Trees are sometimes planted on sites lacking top-soil, or where bad handling of the top-soil has caused denitrification. If there are no other hindrances to tree growth, then fertilising, particularly with nitrogen, is beneficial. However, on most disturbed sites the overriding problems are soil compaction, waterlogging after rain,

Table 4 The effect of three weeding regimes on first season's growth and foliar nutrient concentrations of Wild cherry transplants

	Mown sward	Unmown sward	Bare soil
Height growth (cm)	9	31	80
Diameter growth (mm)	3	7	14
Foliar nutrient concentrations (% dry weight)			
N	2.6	2.5	3.4
P	0.19	0.17	0.20
K	1.06	1.05	1.64

This experiment was planted in April 1982 on a silty clay loam with a grassy sward at Alice Holt, Hampshire. Paraquat was used to keep the bare soil plots weed-free. Foliage samples were collected in August 1982 for nutrient analysis. Regular mowing may have slightly accelerated nutrient cycling, but uptake by the trees was much greater where the weeds were killed.

Table 5 The effect of three weeding regimes, each with and without fertiliser, on first three seasons' growth of oak and ash transplants

	Control: no weeding	0.5 × 0.5 m bituminised felt 'Tree spats'	0.5 m diameter herbicide spots
Oak			
Height growth (cm)			
No Fertiliser	−4	7	45
Fertiliser	−9	8	59
Diameter growth (mm)			
No Fertiliser	5.1	6.6	13.6
Fertiliser	3.6	6.9	16.7
Ash			
Height growth (cm)			
No Fertiliser	18	31	74
Fertiliser	16	48	81
Diameter growth (mm)			
No Fertiliser	3.9	7.7	13.9
Fertiliser	4.5	11.1	15.9

This experiment was planted in March 1982 in Wormwood Scrubs Park, West London on a grassy site that had been regularly mown and used for informal recreation for many years. 'Tree spats' are made from roofing felt. Herbicide spots were kept fairly weed-free with glyphosate, paraquat and propyzamide. Fertilised trees received 45 g of a 9:25:25 (NPK) compound in April 1982 and 40 g of a 27:5:5 compound in April 1983. The 'Tree spats' and herbicide spots gave some relief from weed interference, but were not really large enough.

and drought; until these are solved young trees are more likely to be harmed than helped by fertiliser. Paradoxically it is generally easier to improve tree growth by fertilising on fertile sites than on infertile disturbed sites.

It is sometimes said that young trees should not be fertilised until the year after planting, allowing them time to establish their root system. Since it is easy to 'scorch' newly planted trees with fertiliser and they are unlikely to die for want of nutrients this is sound advice. (On some extremely infertile heaths, pines and spruces have survived for over 50 years and are still under 2 metres tall.) However, if trees are carefully handled between lifting from the nursery bed and replanting, they are encouraged to make early root growth and often will benefit from fertiliser given at planting; but the weeds must first be killed.

Nitrogen fixation by legumes

Leguminous ground-cover species, such as lupins and clover, may be grown to increase the nitrogen content of deficient soils. They do this by fixing atmospheric nitrogen. But they can be extremely harmful to young trees. In one experiment clover proved as detrimental to first-year tree growth as a grassy sward (Table 1); in the second year, trees in clover grew better than those in grass, probably because the grass resumed growth in March, while the clover was inactive until May giving the trees in the clover an interference-free start to the season.

Competition for light

In addition to their roots competing for moisture and nutrients the aerial parts of weeds also interfere with tree growth in a variety of ways. Most obviously, tall weeds compete with small trees for light.

Although photosynthesis, and thus overall growth, is reduced by shading, young plants of many tree species make most height growth at less than full sunlight; but root growth and stem diameter growth are reduced by shading. The filtering by weeds' foliage of particular wavelengths of light can further etiolate young trees growing in their shade.

However, on most landscape-tree planting sites in Britain competition for light appears to be relatively unimportant compared with underground interference. Cutting weeds to prevent shading usually has little effect, whereas killing the weeds, which prevents both shading and root interference, increases tree growth. Indeed regular mowing of a grassy sward can, by maintaining its vigour, result in very dry soil and stunted tree growth. Many experiments illustrate these points. For example, in Table 1, growth of Silver maple in mown and unmown grass was very similar, and poor; but when the vegetation around the base of the trees was killed, they grew well. In Table 4, the Wild cherry grew better in unmown grass than mown grass; this was probably because, as shown in Figure 1, the availability of soil moisture was greater beneath unmown than mown grass.

Foresters sometimes assert that 'weeds' are beneficial in dry sunny weather by providing a humid micro-climate for the tree and protecting it from desiccation. This assertion is perhaps true *if* the only choice is whether or not to mow the weeds, but the benefits of shelter are unlikely to outweigh root interference. The assertion may also owe something to casual observations concentrating on height growth and ignoring stem diameter and root growth. Even if the trees are found to grow best in areas of tall weed growth, it is naive to assume that the weeds have helped the trees; both weeds and trees were probably helped by the better soil in those areas.

Physical damage to the tree

The aerial parts of weeds may physically damage young trees. Woody climbers, such as Old man's beard and honeysuckle, are uncommon on landscape-tree planting sites; but if they are present Old man's beard will grow over, fall down on, and distort small trees; and honeysuckle twines around trees causing spiral distortions when the trees grow. More commonly, herbaceous weeds collapse on small trees in winter and push them over, especially if there is snow. However, considerable root interference will have occurred long before weeds threaten to physically damage young trees.

In addition to physically damaging trees, weeds may also modify tree growth by providing mechanical support. It is known that support, for example by staking, increases height growth and reduces stem diameter growth. This effect and the effect of shade described in the previous section are responsible for the tall thin form of trees growing in dense thickets. Trees often grow taller but thinner in uncut than cut weeds.

Table 6 The effect of four different weeding regimes on vole damage to, and survival of, sycamore transplants

	Diameter of weed-free spot (m)			
	0	0.25	0.5	1
Percentage of trees with some vole damage by September 1983	86	86	75	47
Percentage survival at September 1983	81	66	92	97
Percentage survival at September 1984	42	48	81	94

This experiment was planted in February 1982 at the M3–M25 motorway interchange in Surrey. Spots of 0.25, 0.5 and 1 m diameter were kept moderately weed-free with propyzamide and paraquat. Some trees recorded as vole damaged had only slight damage; others, particularly those in the control treatment and 0.25 m diameter spots, had severe damage. Many trees in these treatments were only just alive in September 1983 and died in the following year. Not all the deaths were caused by voles; trees in the 0.25 m diameter spots suffered accidental paraquat damage.

Weeds can have less direct effects on young trees. On grassy sites, Short-tailed voles often damage or kill young trees by gnawing the bark of the lower stem or roots, but they appear reluctant to cross weed-free ground to reach the tree, presumably because they would be visible to predators; (the sycamore in Table 6 that received little or no weed control suffered more vole damage than the well-weeded trees, and as a result many of them died). Similarly slugs and snails can severely damage leaves and young shoots of small trees, especially if weed growth covers the tree retarding evaporation of rain and dew; a weed-free tree dries more quickly and suffers less damage. Mowing machines frequently inflict bark wounds on trees, and small trees may be cut down if they are not seen; such damage is less likely if an area around the base of each tree is kept free of vegetation. Conversely, damage by hares or vandals may be greater if weeds are removed or mown rather than left to disguise the young trees.

Production of toxins by weeds

The influence of chemicals produced by one plant on another plant is called allelopathy. Possibly the best known example is that of juglone produced by Black walnut which has caused tomatoes, potatoes, apple trees and some pine species to wilt or die. It is said that many other species including grasses, other herbs, ferns and mosses produce allelopathic effects on a wide variety of test species including young plants of some tree species. These reported effects are usually harmful but sometimes helpful to the test species. However, it is very difficult to prove that allelopathy occurs under field conditions. Even when a chemical is collected from one plant, identified and applied to another plant at a naturally occurring concentration, and is shown to have an effect on that plant, sceptics still find alternative hypotheses to explain the result: it could be caused by the artificial conditions necessarily employed in such experiments. These sceptics say that allelopathy is probably uncommon.

Advocates broaden the concept to include effects produced by and on fungi and bacteria. Microbes feeding on dead plant material could, for example, have an allelopathic effect on a tree's mycorrhizal fungi and thus affect the tree. Bearing in mind the vast array of chemicals that are continually being produced, released and broken down into other chemicals in the soil the advocates may be correct in believing allelopathy to be widespread. Although the results of the weeding experiments described in this Handbook are believed to be primarily due to competition for moisture and nutrients, it is possible that allelopathy has also played a part.

Soil and air temperature

Weeds can influence tree growth by their effects on soil and air temperatures. Root growth is very dependent on soil temperature. Living or dead vegetation, or a thick mulch, insulates the soil,

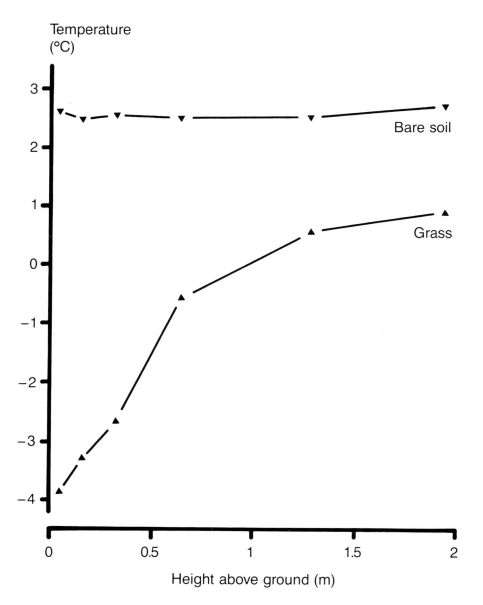

FIGURE 7
The influence of grass on night-time
minimum air temperature.

Taken from Low and Greig (1973). Mean
minimum temperatures are for seven nights
between 28 May and 3 June 1966 on a site in
Thetford Chase, East Anglia.

keeping it cooler in summer and warmer in winter; daily temperature variation is also reduced. But over a whole year it is unclear whether the soil temperatures under bare soil or weeds are most favourable for root growth. Bare soil is probably best since the higher soil temperatures in early spring aid root regeneration by newly planted trees. Most sheet mulching materials, however, significantly raise soil temperatures.

The insulating effect of vegetation reduces radiation heat losses from the soil. Night-time air temperatures in calm weather are therefore lower over vegetation than bare soil (Figure 7). Weed-free trees may thus escape the frost damage suffered by unweeded trees. However, if the trees are completely covered by other vegetation they will be protected.

Young trees growing in dense vegetation may be killed by fire. If each tree has its own fire-break they are more likely to escape.

Factors that modify the influence of weeds on trees

The influence of climate and soil on weed competition for moisture and nutrients has already been discussed. Other factors that may modify the influence of weeds on trees are discussed below.

Weed species

Are all weeds equally harmful to young trees? Grasses are among the most harmful; they grow throughout the year whenever the temperature is not too low, starting before and finishing after active tree growth. With other ground-cover species, trees may get a relatively interference-free period of growth while the ground flora is inactive. However, other herbs, if they are vigorous, can be as harmful as grasses; (the effect of clover on tree growth, shown in Table 1, has already been noted). Woody weeds are often rather less harmful, but well-established coppice stools with their large root systems interfere with trees some distance away. A complete ground cover of vigorous woody shrubs, such as Rose of Sharon or *Cotoneaster* species, is probably very detrimental.

If trees are planted into plots on which different ground-cover species have been established, tree performance (growth or survival or both) appears to be inversely related to the vigour of the ground-cover flora. The flora's leaf area index (leaf area per unit area of ground) gives a crude index of its harmfulness to

young trees. However, if comparisons are made between trees growing in different soils, or different patches of naturalised vegetation on a non-uniform site, then trees are often found to have performed best where the ground flora is most vigorous. Thus, sparse weak weeds on a sand are more harmful than lush vigorous weeds on a loam; this is because of the greater moisture and nutrient reserves to be shared between trees and weeds on the better soil.

Tree species

Are all trees equally harmed by weeds? Although trees differ in the way they respond to weeds, all broadleaved species tested on landscape-tree planting sites have grown much better with effective weeding. The evidence for conifers is less complete, but there is no reason to believe they would behave very differently under the same conditions (see Plates 5–8).

Growth differences between weeded and unweeded trees of vigorous species, such as Wild cherry or ash, are usually clearly visible before the end of their first growing season. With less vigorous species, such as oak, the differences may not become apparent until the second season. But after, say, 5 years the differences between weeded and unweeded trees are often smaller with the more vigorous species; unweeded trees of these species often start to grow well after a year or two despite the weeds, whereas growth of less vigorous species remains checked by weeds for many years. So after one season ash appears to be more harmed by weeds than oak, but after five seasons the situation may be reversed.

Oak often makes little height growth unless it has side shelter. Weeding usually increases its leaf area, nutrient uptake, root growth and diameter growth, but height growth may not be improved for some years. Height differences of other species appear sooner.

Sometimes weeds reduce the survival of one species but not another. Often this is because plants of the first species were of inferior quality, and not because that species is inherently more sensitive to weeds. Even if initial survival of all species is good, that of species whose growth remains checked by weeds for many years is likely to decline as voles and other damaging agents take their toll.

Stock type

Are large standards and small seedlings equally susceptible to weed interference? Obviously standard trees do not experience

PLATES 5, 6, 7 & 8

Sitka spruce photographed in January 1987, 10 months after planting as 31 cm transplants in a weeding experiment on a silt loam in Tintern Forest, Gwent.

Left – no weed control;

Above – mown weeds; notice the poor needle colour of the spruce;

Opposite left – a 1 × 1 m area weeded with glyphosate herbicide in 1986;

Opposite right – a 1 × 1 m black polythene mulch.

Only the spruce with herbicide or polythene treatment made a second burst of growth in 1986.

Table 7 The effect of chemical weeding on survival and height of transplants, whips and light standards of hornbeam, oak and rowan after three seasons

	Survival after three seasons (%)		Height (cm)		
			Initial	After three seasons	
	Control	Herbicide		Control	Herbicide
Hornbeam					
Transplants	17	69	58	77	112
Whips	2	40	139	29	82
Standards	56	90	188	120	181
Oak					
Transplants	83	96	67	57	111
Whips	44	90	113	76	127
Standards	31	83	228	147	214
Rowan					
Transplants	96	96	48	94	164
Whips	98	90	89	117	173
Standards	96	100	215	225	258

This experiment was planted in March 1984 on a clayey soil with a grassy sward beside the M11 motorway near Epping, Essex. Chemically weeded trees had 1.2 m diameter spots kept fairly weed-free with glyphosate. In summer 1984 the soil became very dry, large cracks appeared and the trees suffered badly. Many trees died or died-back. For each species, all the plants came from the same nursery in an attempt to achieve some comparability between the three sizes of tree. However, they inevitably had different nursery histories, so any comparisons between the three sizes must be very tentative.

competition for light, but their growth, and often survival also, is greatly reduced by subterranean interference. (In the experiment referred to in Table 7 the survival and growth of standards, whips and transplants of oak and hornbeam were all reduced by weeds; with the rowan, only growth was reduced.) All sizes of stock – seedlings, transplants, whips and standards – and all types of stock – bare-rooted, container-grown and unrooted cuttings – are harmed by weeds.

Quality of plants and planting

Are good and poor quality plants equally susceptible to weed interference? Tree growth, even of good quality trees that have been carefully planted, is almost invariably reduced by weeds. Survival, though, is usually only reduced when the trees are under

some additional stress. This extra stress may be caused by poor planting, delay between lifting in the nursery and replanting, desiccation or heat while the plants are out of the ground, poor soil conditions, or drought.

Tree shelters

Do tree shelters, by providing a humid micro-climate and so reducing the tree's water needs, obviate the need to weed? No; trees in shelters and those outside respond similarly to weed interference. (Figures 8 and 9 show the results of a weeding experiment in which half of the trees were in shelters.) Shelters are no substitute for effective weeding, but they do make herbicide application easier, trees being protected from accidental damage.

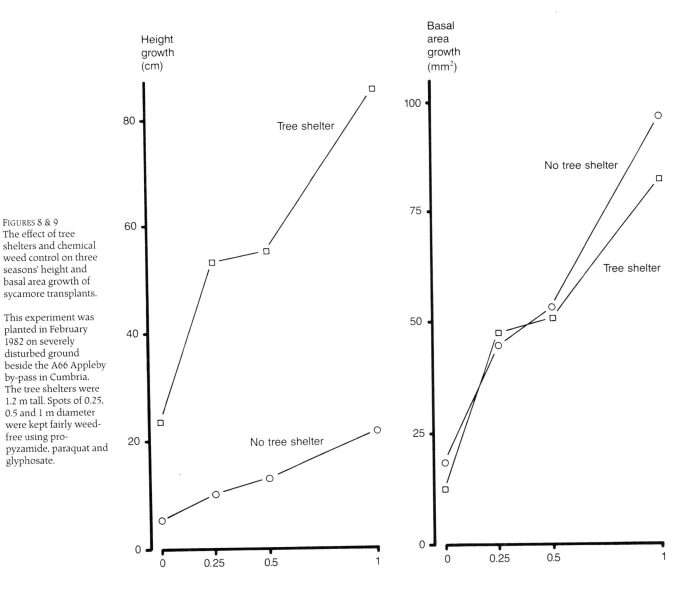

FIGURES 8 & 9
The effect of tree shelters and chemical weed control on three seasons' height and basal area growth of sycamore transplants.

This experiment was planted in February 1982 on severely disturbed ground beside the A66 Appleby by-pass in Cumbria. The tree shelters were 1.2 m tall. Spots of 0.25, 0.5 and 1 m diameter were kept fairly weed-free using pro-pyzamide, paraquat and glyphosate.

Height growth (cm)

Tree shelter

No tree shelter

Basal area growth (mm^2)

No tree shelter

Tree shelter

Diameter of weed-free area at base of tree (m)

Methods of weed control

Having discussed *how* weeds interfere with young trees, we can now consider the practicalities of controlling them. Various weeding methods are considered first.

Mowing

Cutting grassy swards by tractor-mounted swipe, mowing machine, strimmer or sickle is more likely to harm than help the tree. Mowing enhances the appearance of the sward, but not of the tree (Plate 10) and is ineffective as a weeding method. With other weed types it may reduce root interference but never eliminates it. Trees are often accidentally damaged when adjacent vegetation is being cut.

The various plants in the weed flora interfere with one another as well as with trees. Mowing changes the balance between the various species in favour of the grasses, which are resistant to cutting; other weed species therefore decline. In this way mowing creates a grassy weed flora that is very harmful to trees. Unmown weeds often die-back and produce a self-mulching effect in winter, giving trees an interference-free start to the next season; trees in a mown sward do not enjoy this mulching effect.

Cultivation

Ploughing, hoeing and similar techniques cut weeds below ground level, uproot and leave them to desiccate, or may bury them. However, some weeds, Couch grass for example, regenerate speedily from cut rhizomes. Fertile soils may contain tens of thousands of weed seeds per square metre, some of which are brought to the surface and germinate, every time the soil is cultivated. Cultivation is a better weeding method in countries with a Mediterranean climate (little or no summer rainfall) where seed brought to the surface in summer can not germinate successfully, and uprooted weeds and rhizomes soon wither.

Ploughing before planting is relatively cheap, and as well as providing initial weed control it also improves the ease and quality of planting. Planting-pit preparation is more expensive and the sizes usually employed (300 mm diameter pits are common for transplants) are much too small to prevent weed interference. On some infertile sites pre-planting ploughing is all that is required, but on most sites further weeding is needed. Cultivation by hoe or mattock, with care to minimise damage to tree roots, can be very effective; this was shown in a number of early Forestry Commission experiments, conducted before the advent of herbicides, in which broadleaved trees grew much better when weeded by hoe than by sickle. (Table 8 refers to three of these experiments, and also shows, as noted earlier, that compared with most other species oak's height growth is relatively unresponsive to weeding treatments. Only height was measured in these experiments.) Hoeing, however, being laborious and therefore expensive was never adopted in the forest, but it is appropriate for small planting schemes in parks and gardens. In damp seasons fertile sites may require seven or more hoeings a year to keep them reasonably weed-free.

Herbicides

Chemical weed control is less laborious than hoeing and requires fewer repetitions to achieve the same degree of control. There are many different herbicides, no two having identical properties, and new herbicides are continually being developed. One can not be familiar with them all, but a small armoury, of perhaps three to six herbicides, meets most tree-planters' needs.

The following paragraphs introduce some herbicides to illustrate the various ways in which they work. More detailed information on these and other herbicides can be found in FC Booklet 51 *The use of herbicides in the forest* (Sale, Tabbush and Lane, 1986) which also covers application methods and equipment, safety clothing and precautions, and calibration to ensure that the correct dose is applied. However, the most important reading is on the herbicide container's label – these instructions should always be carefully read and followed.

PLATE 9
Young trees with healthy new growth and foliage, because they have been properly weeded.

PLATE 10
Another expensive eyesore. If the grass had been killed rather than mown this tree would be carrying more foliage and have less die-back in the crown.

Table 8 The effect of 'weeding' by sickle, which merely cuts the tops off the weeds, and hoeing on height growth in three early experiments

Forest name and experiment number	Friston 14	Micheldever 1	Dean 36
County	E. Sussex	Hampshire	Gloucestershire
Species	Beech	Oak	Ash
Years hoed (inclusive)	5th–7th	1st–3rd	1st–3rd
Age when assessed (years)	11	7	4
Height (cm)			
Sickle	99	106	44
Hoe	188	119	80

Taken from Davies (1985).

Residual herbicides are taken up from the soil by weed roots. They must be selective since weed and tree roots occupy the same soil. Propyzamide is an example – trees are tolerant, but most grasses and some germinating seeds are killed. If the weed flora contains grasses and broadleaved weeds, the latter will be invigorated by removal of the grass, and a different herbicide will be needed for the next application.

Atrazine is another residual herbicide although it also enters through foliage, and must therefore be applied carefully. Its selectivity, like that of many residual herbicides, is very dose-dependent. At the correct application rate most grasses and some other herbs are controlled, but if this is exceeded broadleaved trees and some conifers will be damaged or killed by root uptake.

Simazine, also a residual herbicide, kills germinating seeds rather then established weeds and is therefore used to prevent reinvasion of weed-free soil*. At high doses it acts as a total

herbicide, killing established plants. It usually stays close to the soil surface until it breaks down, but under certain soil and weather conditions it may move down to the tree roots and damage or kill sensitive broadleaved species.

Contact herbicides are absorbed by leaves and shoots; most affect a wide spectrum of plants, trees as well as weeds, and must therefore be applied selectively. They may be applied at a time of year when the trees are tolerant but the weeds sensitive, or they may be applied to the weeds only, the trees being avoided or guarded. One disadvantage of contact herbicides is that the weeds must be left to grow some foliage before treatment, by which time interference with the tree has already begun.

Paraquat is a contact herbicide. It quickly kills any green foliage that it touches, but is inactivated in soil. It is not translocated within the plant, so its effect may be transitory, weeds regenerating from unaffected roots. Glyphosate is a translocated contact herbicide; if a sufficient quantity enters the weed the whole plant is killed. Most contact herbicides are rapidly inactivated or broken down in soil.

Herbicides generally work better at some times of year than others. Propyzamide, for example, only works in cold soil and is therefore applied in winter. Glyphosate works best when weeds are growing actively. Some conifers tolerate glyphosate once the current year's growth has hardened off and it does not matter if

---

*The experiments described in this Handbook relied heavily on contact herbicides; simazine was not used although it undoubtedly could have improved the degree of control achieved and so reduced the number of herbicide applications needed. Simazine was not used because the experiments were designed to examine the need to weed, rather than looking for economical methods of weed control, and it was therefore necessary to avoid the possibility of residual effects on the trees.

PLATE 11
Hoeing is laborious, but may be appropriate for small planting schemes in parks and gardens. Care is needed to avoid damaging the tree roots.

PLATE 12
Herbicides are the most economical method of weed control for many planting schemes. Protective clothing appropriate to the herbicide and the application method must be worn.

they receive some of the spray intended for the weeds, but usually it must be kept off the trees.

Spraying in windy weather increases the risk of accidental damage to trees from contact herbicides. In dry weather some residual herbicides may be inactivated by sunlight before they are washed into the soil. Rain falling soon after the application of a contact herbicide may wash it off the weeds before they have been killed. In general, weather conditions are more critical for the application of contact herbicides, but soil conditions are of greater importance with residuals. Both trees and weeds are particularly sensitive to residuals in coarse-textured soils containing little organic matter.

As with hoeing, herbicides frequently cause some damage to the tree. However, if they are applied with reasonable care, any damage is far outweighed by the relief from weed interference.

Application methods

Granular herbicides are often applied from a 'pepperpot', a hand-held container with holes. Liquid formulations may be applied by tractor-mounted boom sprayers, knapsack sprayers or direct applicators. The latter deliver herbicide from a saturated wick which contacts the weeds. The operator can see where the herbicide is going and there is no risk of drift, but it can be difficult to control the application rate. However, application rates are less critical with the contact herbicides used in direct applicators than with residual herbicides. Application rates are harder to control in irregularly spaced landscape plantings than forests and agricultural crops.

Safety of herbicides

Many landscape trees are planted in areas accessible to the public and also in private gardens. Do herbicides on these sites pose any danger to man or the environment? The only significant dangers arise through incorrect application and accidents. Spillages are most likely during mixing prior to use, so this should be done in the depot rather than the park. Operators should be properly trained in all aspects of herbicide use including what to do in the unlikely event of a spillage and how to safely dispose of any surpluses. Herbicides must be stored safely and steps taken to prevent them ever falling into children's hands.

But what if a child or dog ate some recently sprayed weeds? Precautions, such as the erection of warning notices in public areas, should be taken to lessen this risk. However, even with paraquat, one of the more poisonous herbicides, unrealistically large quantities of weed would need to be eaten before any harm arose *provided* that the application rate was correct.

When properly applied any direct effects of herbicides on wildlife (excluding weeds) are minute compared to the indirect effects. All weeding methods have indirect effects on wildlife; the removal of some plants, even if they are simply pulled out by hand, radically alters the micro-environment causing the decrease of some and increase of other organisms.

Protective clothing appropriate to the herbicide and application method is especially important when operators use herbicides regularly. But the appearance in public areas of 'spacemen' wearing protective suits and face masks may cause alarm. This can be reduced by telling the public what is happening and why, and by keeping them a suitable distance away during application.

Under the Control of Pesticides Regulations 1986 every herbicide is subjected to rigorous scrutiny before it is approved for sale in the UK. These Regulations, which were made under the Food and Environment Protection Act 1985, are enforced by the Pesticides Registration and Surveillance Department of the Ministry of Agriculture, Fisheries and Food. They ensure that all agrochemicals sold in the UK are both safe and effective. Poisonous herbicides, such as paraquat, may not be sold to the general public in concentrated formulations. But it is not just the sale of herbicides that is controlled: all users must comply with the conditions of approval relating to the herbicide they are using. These conditions, which are clearly stated on the label, define the situations in which the herbicide may be used, the method of application, the maximum permitted application rate, and the protective clothing to be worn.

Mulching

Since most soil moisture is lost by transpiration, the primary way in which mulching conserves moisture for the tree is by suppressing weeds; this is the mulch's main function. But mulches also reduce the smaller losses which occur by evaporation from bare soil (Figure 1). By keeping the surface soil moist, where most of the plant-available nutrients are found, mulching helps maintain nutrient availability. On readily leached sandy soils impermeable sheet mulches reduce nutrient loss in wet weather. Sheet mulches also raise soil temperatures and thus stimulate root growth.

The relative importance of these soil moisture, nutrient and temperature effects for tree growth is usually impossible to determine and no doubt varies with site and species. But the improvement in tree survival is often dramatic, especially on soils with very poor moisture retention (Table 2), or where the trees are already under some other stress perhaps through poor handling between the nursery and replanting. The oak used in the experiment referred to in Figure 10 were very weak plants: no unweeded trees survived the first season; but the further weeds were kept from the trees, whether by polythene mulches or herbicides, the more trees survived. Even if survival without mulching is good, nutrition is usually improved, and tree growth is almost always enhanced. In the experiments referred to in Figures 11 and 12, trees grew better the larger the polythene mulching mat.

Mulching can, however, cause problems. On poorly drained sites the reduced evaporation may exacerbate any waterlogging, causing anaerobic soil conditions which can kill trees (Table 3); such sites should be drained before planting, and then mulching would be beneficial. Voles sometimes nest under sheet mulches and gnaw trees below the sheet, even felling small trees; such

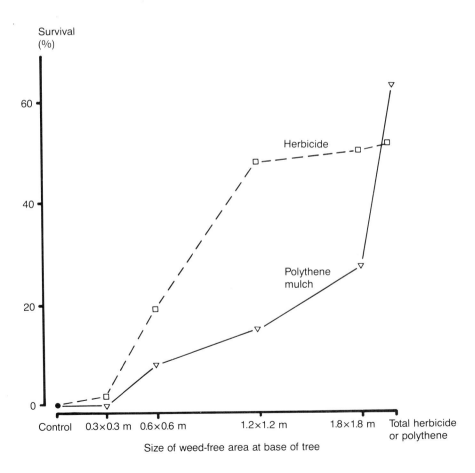

FIGURE 10
The effect of chemical weed control and black polythene mulching on first-year survival of poor quality oak transplants.

The oak had many dead and damaged roots, and the small buds indicated that they had not thrived in the previous year in the nursery. A site with a fine-textured soil and grassy sward at Quedgeley, Gloucestershire was used for this experiment which was planted in March 1984. Square polythene mulches were 0.3 × 0.3, 0.6 × 0.6, 1.2 × 1.2 and 1.8 × 1.8 m. Trees were planted at 2 × 2 m. In the total polythene treatment 12 trees were planted into each 10 × 8 m mulch sheet. Glyphosate was applied to areas of the same size and shape in the herbicide treatments.

damage can be greatly reduced by placing clods of earth or other weights on the sheet, close to the tree.

Many materials are used as mulches. Traditionally, organic materials such as bark, peat, straw or leaves were used. Gravel can also be used. Unless they are killed before mulch is applied, vigorous weeds are able to grow through even a 100 mm mulch (Plate 13). New weeds germinating in the mulch are easier to control, being readily uprooted. Fresh bark contains volatile oils which are toxic to plants; bark for horticultural use is composted first, which reduces the concentration of these oils to sub-phytotoxic levels. Materials with a high carbon:nitrogen ratio, such as bark, wood chips and straw, can induce nitrogen deficiency in mulched plants and nitrogenous fertiliser may be needed. Alkaline materials, such as spent mushroom compost, can induce iron and manganese deficiency.

Many sheet materials such as polythene, old carpets and roofing felt can be used as a mulch. The sheet must remain intact if it is to suppress weeds. It is desirable that little or no light penetrates the sheet; light allows weeds to grow under the sheet which may interfere with the tree or dislodge the sheet. In hot sunny weather clear polythene can result in very high soil temperatures and trees may be killed. Old carpets and roofing felt are often heavy enough to require no further anchorage, but polythene sheets must be secured by burying the corners and placing clods of earth or other weights on top.

Black polythene is a good mulch. Its cost is closely related to the thickness of the film, but thicker films are easier to handle and less likely to be torn by stones or animals; foxes and cats sometimes scratch at voles nesting beneath sheet mulches (Plate 14). On rough sites 125μm thickness is usually needed, but where less strength is required 40μm is sufficient. The chemical composition of the sheet is, however, more important than its thickness. Some polythenes quickly become brittle in sunlight; only film made from virgin polymer, rather than recycled material, should be used; and it should contain between 2 and 5 per cent carbon-black; this gives the film both its colour and ultra-violet stability. Material sold for mulching should have a suitable composition, but other polythene sheets may not last long in sunlight. Sheet mulching materials can be unsightly. If vegetation around the sheet is left uncut it will fall on the sheet and hide it. Alternatively the sheet can be covered with a thin layer of gravel or bark. A covering on top of a polythene mulch will also help to anchor it and will protect if from ultra-violet light.

PLATE 13
An ineffective bark mulch which has been quickly colonised by weeds; supplementary action with hoe or herbicides is needed.

PLATE 14
Foxes have torn this black polythene mulch. They were hunting for voles nesting beneath it. Unless it is repaired, weeds will grow through the holes.

Alternative ground-cover species

Is it possible to find ground covers, wild flowers or non-competitive grasses perhaps, that will not harm young trees? Earlier, it was suggested that the harmfulness of the weed flora depends on (a) its growth periodicity – ground-cover species that are inactive for part of the tree's growing season appear less harmful than those with a longer growing period – and (b) its vigour or leaf area. But, ground covers that do not make full use of the site and the growing season are usually invaded by other more vigorous and harmful species. However, since trees are most sensitive to weed interference in their first spring and early summer after planting, trees planted into a non-vigorous ground cover may be fairly well established before more vigorous weeds colonise the site; but they are unlikely to fare better than if they were planted into bare soil.

Certain mosses are resistant to some herbicides and may form a mat on regularly treated ground. Because they do not have roots they take little moisture from the soil and do not appear to interfere much with young trees. Indeed they can be useful in stabilising the surface soil and protecting it from rain-drop impact. However, they are not generally considered attractive enough for use as alternative ground-cover species.

Area of weed control

How large an area should be kept weed-free at the base of the tree? The answer depends on at least three factors.

1. What rate of tree growth is sought?
2. How large a vegetation-free area is aesthetically and environmentally acceptable? On some sites large bare areas could suffer soil erosion.
3. What is an acceptable weeding cost? Although larger areas cost more, doubling the area treated per tree does not double the total cost; costs of mulch or herbicide are doubled, but labour costs, which are usually greater, are not.

The larger the weed-free area, the faster trees grow. Clearly though, there must be some distance beyond which weeds do not interfere with the tree. However, even in its first year, a tree's growth can be checked by weeds one metre away. Survival is also sometimes related to the weed-free area. Figures 4, 5, 8, 9, 10, 11 and 12 and Tables 1, 2 and 6 refer to experiments in each of which trees grew or survived better with larger rather than smaller areas kept weed-free at their base. These experiments were conducted on both man-made and undisturbed sites, with sandy, loamy and clayey soils.

Figures 11 and 12 refer to experiments comparing different sizes of black polythene mulching mats and herbicide spots. In these and other similar experiments trees have grown better with herbicide spots than polythene mats of the same size when the area has been less than about one metre diameter. With larger treated areas tree growth is better with mulching mats than with herbicide spots. Weeds around the edge of a mulching mat are invigorated by it, root under it and interfere with the tree; trees therefore perform much better if weeds surrounding the mulch are killed, a point clearly shown in Figures 11 and 12.

As a general rule an area of at least 1.0 m diameter at the base of transplants and 1.5 m diameter for standards should be kept weed-free. The attraction of using polythene mats in extensive planting schemes is that, unlike herbicides, once applied they provide weed suppression over a number of seasons; in these schemes mats should be at least 1.0 m diameter. In more intensively managed schemes mats may be used primarily to reduce the risk of herbicide damage which may occur when weeds very close to the tree are treated; smaller mats are then appropriate.

Perforated mats to help rain reach the soil are sometimes advocated; but weeds readily grow through many perforated sheets; and even when the perforations are too small to permit weed penetration, the extra light reaching the soil may allow weeds to grow beneath the sheet. Also, soil moisture assessments under 10×8 m sheets of unperforated polythene, such as that shown in Plate 18, indicate that although trees dry the soil under the sheet, it does re-wet again within a few days of rain falling. It is not always clear how the water gets under these large sheets, but get there it does. Since the soil under very large unperforated sheets re-wets so readily, problems are most unlikely to occur with smaller mats. Perforations are unnecessary.

Timing of weed control

Weed control should start before the trees are planted when there is no risk of damaging them with contact herbicides or cultivation implements. If serious weed problems are expected it may be

PLATES 15, 16, 17 & 18
Sycamore photographed in July 1985, 16 months after planting as 42 cm transplants on an infertile sand.

Upper left – no weed control;

Upper right – a 1.2 × 1.2 m area kept weed-free with herbicides;

Lower left – a 1.2 × 1.2 m black polythene mulch;

Lower right – a very large, 10 × 8 m, black polythene mulch.

On impoverished sites such as this even sparse weed growth is highly detrimental. (See also Figure 11 which refers to the same experiment.)

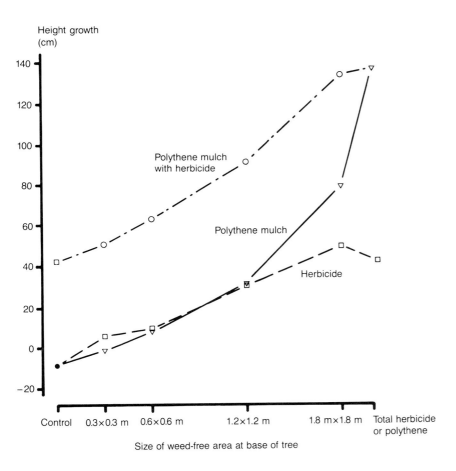

Height growth (cm)

Size of weed-free area at base of tree

FIGURE 11
The effect of chemical weed control and black polythene mulching (with or without the remainder of the vegetation in the plot treated with herbicide) on 3 years' height growth of sycamore transplants.

A site with a coarse-textured soil and grassy sward at Hankley Common, Surrey was used for this experiment which was planted in March 1984. Square polythene mulches were 0.3 × 0.3, 0.6 × 0.6, 1.2 × 1.2 and 1.8 × 1.8 m. Paraquat and glyphosate kept areas of the same size and shape fairly weed-free in the herbicide treatments. Trees were planted at 2 × 2 m with 12 trees in each plot. In some plots all the vegetation between the square mulches was treated with herbicide. In the total polythene treatment 12 trees were planted into each 10 × 8 m mulch sheet. (Reduced growth in the total herbicide treatment was probably caused by accidental damage.) (See also Plates 15, 16, 17 and 18.)

best to delay planting for a year, and first tackle the weeds with a combination of cultivations and herbicide applications.

Interference from weeds is usually most severe in April, May and June. If weeding is delayed until mid-summer, the weeds will be well established and hard to kill without damaging the tree and most of the interference for that year will have already occurred. Over most of England soil moisture deficits start to develop in April; transpiration from any weeds remaining after this date, even if they are killed in May, results in larger deficits for the whole growing season. So one week's weed growth in April may reduce moisture availability right through to October. Weed control must therefore begin early in the year. Given a weed-free start trees make early root growth and withstand some weed reinvasion later in the season, although they grow best if kept weed-free through the growing season.

Weed growth in one year rarely, if ever, reduces moisture availability in the next because winter rain replenishes the soil reservoir. Nevertheless, trees weakened by weeds in one year may in

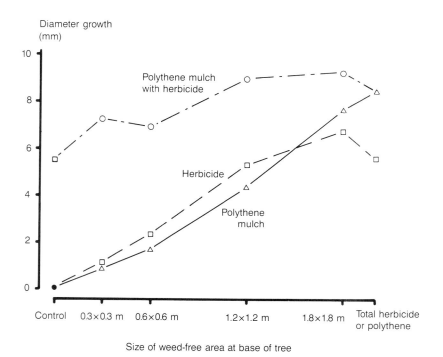

Diameter growth (mm)

Polythene mulch with herbicide

Herbicide

Polythene mulch

Control   0.3×0.3 m   0.6×0.6 m   1.2×1.2 m   1.8×1.8 m   Total herbicide or polythene

Size of weed-free area at base of tree

FIGURE 12
The effect of chemical weed control and black polythene mulching (with or without the remainder of the vegetation in the plot treated with herbicide) on 2 years' diameter growth of Field maple transplants.

A poorly drained site with a fine-textured soil and grassy sward near Bedford was used for this experiment which was planted in March 1984. Square polythene mulches were 0.3 × 0.3, 0.6 × 0.6, 1.2 × 1.2 and 1.8 × 1.8 m. Glyphosate and paraquat kept areas of the same size and shape moderately weed-free in the herbicide treatments. Trees were planted at 2 × 2 m with 12 trees in each plot. In some plots all the vegetation between the mulches was treated with herbicide. In the total polythene treatment 12 trees were planted into each 10 × 8 m mulch sheet. (Reduced growth in the total herbicide treatment was probably caused by accidental damage. Reduced growth in the total polythene treatment was probably caused by somewhat anaerobic soil conditions on this wet site being exacerbated by the mulch.)

subsequent years grow poorly, or even die, despite weeds being removed. The first spring and summer is crucial for newly planted trees. In later years trees withstand interference from weeds better. Three years weeding usually ensures successful tree establishment, provided the site was well prepared and planted with good plants of suitable species; thereafter although weeds still reduce tree growth weeding may not be worthwhile. The number of years through which weeding is necessary is greatly lengthened by inadequate soil preparation, poor plants, the use of species unsuited to the site or any other factor which stresses the tree*. Older trees which are making little growth can sometimes be revived by weeding. Figures 13 and 14 show how

the growth of 10-year-old slow-growing ash in an experiment near Leeds was accelerated by weeding.

The ground under orchard trees is usually kept bare using herbicides throughout the life of the crop since this increases fruit

---

*This Handbook has concentrated on just one aspect of tree establishment – weed control. But no matter how well the weeds are controlled, trees may still die or grow badly if other aspects are neglected. Further information on recommended techniques for tree establishment and protection is contained in FC Bulletin 62 *Silviculture of broadleaved woodland* (Evans, 1984) and FC Bulletin 65 *Advances in practical arboriculture* (Patch, 1987).

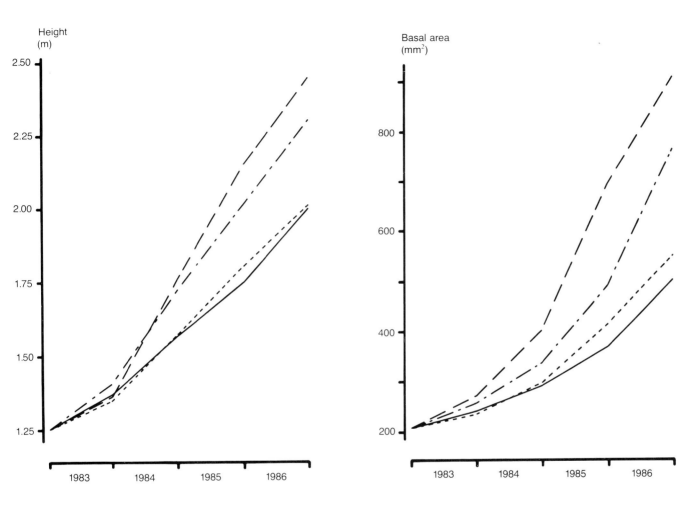

Height
(m)

2.50
2.25
2.00
1.75
1.50
1.25

1983   1984   1985   1986

Basal area
(mm²)

800

600

400

200

1983   1984   1985   1986

——— ——— Herbicide and fertiliser

—·—·—·—· Herbicide

············· Fertiliser

——————— Control

FIGURES 13 & 14
The effect of weeding and fertilising on slow-growing ash.

The ash used in this experiment were planted about 1973 beside the M62
motorway near Leeds. The fine-textured soil had been disturbed during
motorway construction, but developed a vigorous grassy sward. Fertilised
trees received 80 g of NPK (21:14:14) fertiliser in June 1983, April 1984 and
June 1985. Weeded trees had a 1.2 m diameter area kept fairly weed-free
from June 1983 onwards using paraquat and propyzamide in 1983 and
glyphosate in 1985.

production. Under this regime the organic matter content of the soil gradually declines and soil structure may deteriorate. However, with landscape trees weeding should only be necessary for a few years to get them started, and these adverse effects will be negligible.

Degree of weed control

Is it necessary to remove *every* weed from the base of the tree, or can a few be tolerated? From a practical viewpoint it is much easier to tackle weeds before they emerge, or while they are still small and few. Hoeing and herbicide application is quick and easy at this stage; well-established weeds are hard to remove without damaging the tree. A few small weeds enjoy reduced interference from neighbours and often grow quickly. To avoid damaging small trees with contact herbicides if weeds have been left unchecked, it is often necessary to cut the weeds prior to application; it is therefore usually a false economy to delay weeding.

In addition to these practical considerations, a few weeds regenerating after herbicide application or hoeing, or growing through a mulch, can appreciably reduce tree survival and growth, although removal of the bulk of the weeds gives the main benefit. The best plan is to control weeds thoroughly, starting before tree planting, and never to let them get out of control; this greatly reduces the number of years through which weeding is needed.

References

DAVIES, R.J. (1985). The importance of weed control and the use of tree shelters for establishing broadleaved trees on grass-dominated sites in England. *Forestry* **58** (2), 167–180.

EVANS, J. (1984). *Silviculture of broadleaved woodland.* Forestry Commission Bulletin 62. HMSO, London.

HALL, D.G.M., REEVE, M.J., THOMASSON, A.J. AND WRIGHT, V.F. (1977). *Water retention, porosity and density of field soils.* Technical Monograph No. 9. Soil Survey of England and Wales, Harpenden.

LOW, J.D. AND GREIG, B.J.W. (1973). Spring frosts affecting the establishment of second rotation crops in Thetford Chase. *Forestry* **46** (2), 139–155.

PATCH, D. (ed.) (1987). *Advances in practical arboriculture.* Forestry Commission Bulletin 65. HMSO, London.

SALE, J.S.P., TABBUSH, P.M. AND LANE, P.B. (1986). *The use of herbicides in the forest* (2nd edn.) Forestry Commission Booklet 51. Forestry Commission, Edinburgh.

Printed in the United Kingdom for Her Majesty's Stationery Office   Dd 239941   7/87
C55   3933/2   4146